ACHIEVE LEVEL 3

MATHEMATICS

By **Louise Moore**

RISING★STARS

Rising Stars UK Ltd, 7 Hatchers Mews, Bermondsey Street, London SE1 3GS

www.risingstars-uk.com

Every effort has been made to trace copyright holders and obtain their permission for the use of copyright material. The authors and publishers will gladly receive information enabling them to rectify any error or omission in subsequent editions.

All facts are correct at time of going to press.

Published 2007
Reprinted 2009, 2010, 2011

British Library Cataloguing in Publication Data
A CIP record for this book is available from the British Library.

ISBN: 978-1-84680-113-6

Printed by Craft Print International Ltd, Singapore

Contents

How to use this book

(1) Introduction – This section tells you what you need to do to achieve a Level 3. It picks out the key learning objective and explains it simply to you.

(2) Question – The question helps you to learn by doing. It is presented in a similar way to a National Tests question and gives you a real example to work with.

(3) Flow chart – This shows you the steps to use when completing questions like this. Some of the advice appears on every flow chart, such as 'read the question, then read it again'. This is because this is the best way of getting good marks on the test.

(4) Tip boxes and Key facts – These provide test hints and general tips on getting the best marks in the tests.

The icon indicates the section is a teaching section.

(5) Practice questions – This is where you have to do the work! Try the question using the technique in the flow chart, then check your answers at the back. Practising questions is the best way to help improve your understanding.

(6) Self assessment – Colour in the face that best describes your understanding of the topic. If you can answer all or nearly all of the questions correctly, colour in a smiling face. If you can answer at least half of the questions correctly, colour in a straight face. If you get more than half of the questions wrong, colour in a down-turned face, then try again!

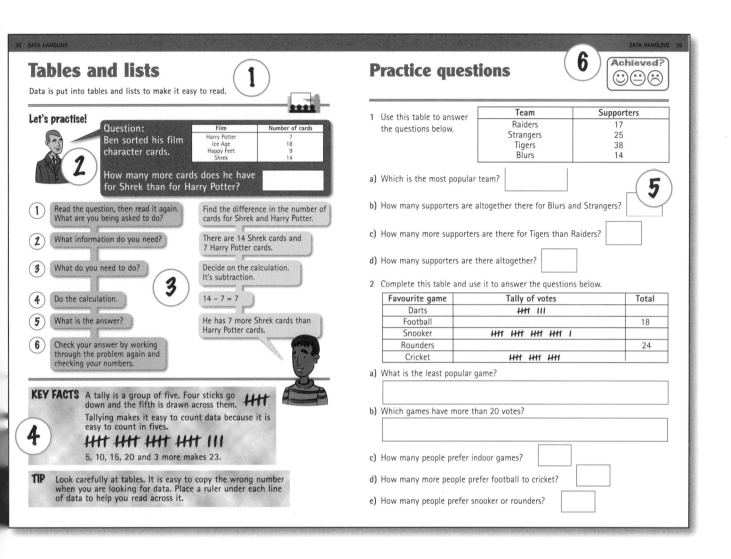

Tables and lists

Data is put into tables and lists to make it easy to read.

Let's practise!

Question:
Ben sorted his film character cards.

Film	Number of cards
Harry Potter	7
Ice Age	18
Happy Feet	9
Shrek	14

How many more cards does he have for Shrek than for Harry Potter?

1. Read the question, then read it again. What are you being asked to do?
2. What information do you need?
3. What do you need to do?
4. Do the calculation.
5. What is the answer?
6. Check your answer by working through the problem again and checking your numbers.

Find the difference in the number of cards for Shrek and Harry Potter.

There are 14 Shrek cards and 7 Harry Potter cards.

Decide on the calculation. It's subtraction.

14 − 7 = 7

He has 7 more Shrek cards than Harry Potter cards.

KEY FACTS A tally is a group of five. Four sticks go down and the fifth is drawn across them. ⊬⊬⊬

Tallying makes it easy to count data because it is easy to count in fives.

⊬⊬⊬ ⊬⊬⊬ ⊬⊬⊬ ⊬⊬⊬ |||

5, 10, 15, 20 and 3 more makes 23.

TIP Look carefully at tables. It is easy to copy the wrong number when you are looking for data. Place a ruler under each line of data to help you read across it.

Practice questions

Achieved? ☺ 😐 ☹

1. Use this table to answer the questions below.

Team	Supporters
Raiders	17
Strangers	25
Tigers	38
Blurs	14

a) Which is the most popular team?

b) How many supporters are altogether there for Blurs and Strangers?

c) How many more supporters are there for Tigers than Raiders?

d) How many supporters are there altogether?

2. Complete this table and use it to answer the questions below.

Favourite game	Tally of votes	Total
Darts	⊬⊬⊬ |||	
Football		18
Snooker	⊬⊬⊬ ⊬⊬⊬ ⊬⊬⊬ ⊬⊬⊬		
Rounders		24
Cricket	⊬⊬⊬ ⊬⊬⊬ ⊬⊬⊬	

a) What is the least popular game?

b) Which games have more than 20 votes?

c) How many people prefer indoor games?

d) How many more people prefer football to cricket?

e) How many people prefer snooker or rounders?

What we have included:

Those topics at Level 2 that are trickiest to get right.

All Level 3 content, so you know that you are covering all the topics that could come up in the test.

We have also put in a big selection of our favourite test techniques, tips for revision and some advice on what the tests are all about, as well as the answers so you can see how well you are getting on.

GOOD LUCK!

Using and applying mathematics

When you have achieved Level 2, you are ready to work on Level 3. These are the main things you should be able to do if you have achieved Level 2 in using and applying mathematics.

Level 2

★ You can select the maths you need for some activities, so you know what to do and how to do it with some of the maths work you are given.

★ When you talk about your work, you use mathematical language. Check that you know the meaning of the following words:

digit	tally	pentagon
number	represents	hexagon
greatest	fraction	clockwise
subtract	multiply	north
minus	multiple	south
operation	row	east
metre	column	west
kilogram	divide	predict
litre	calculate	solve
	surface	

★ You write your work down using symbols (e.g. +, −, x, ÷, =) and simple diagrams
For example: 3 + 12 = 15

★ When you have worked out a problem, you can explain how you did it and why an answer is correct.

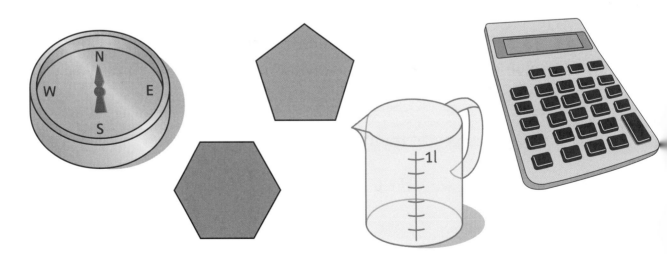

The number system and calculations

These are the main things you should be able to do if you have achieved Level 2 in number and calculating.

Level 2

★ You can count sets of objects in tens, fives or twos several times and always get the right answer.

★ You've learnt the addition and subtraction facts to ten and use them in problems. This means you know the number bonds for every number up to ten. These are the number facts for four:

$0 + 4 = 4$	$4 - 0 = 4$
$1 + 3 = 4$	$4 - 1 = 3$
$2 + 2 = 4$	$4 - 2 = 2$
$3 + 1 = 4$	$4 - 3 = 1$
$4 + 0 = 4$	$4 - 4 = 0$

★ You are beginning to understand the place value of each digit in a number, so you know that 24 means 2 tens and 4 units.

★ You can put numbers up to 100 in order like this:

6   24   51   68   95

smallest ————————————————→ **biggest**

★ When you solve word problems, you can work out whether you need to add or subtract. You know that subtraction is the inverse (or opposite) of addition, so $5 + 3 = 8$ can be written as $8 - 3 = 5$.

★ When you solve number problems involving money and measures, you can do some of them in your head.

★ You recognise sequences of numbers, including odd and even numbers.

★ You can solve missing number problems like $30 - \boxed{6} = 24$.

Shape, space and measures

These are the main things you should be able to do if you have achieved Level 2 in shape, space and measures.

Level 2

★ You know these 3-D and 2-D shapes:

cube cuboid cylinder pyramid	sphere cone circle triangle	square rectangle hexagon	pentagon octagon

★ When describing 3-D and 2-D shapes, you can talk about the faces, the edges, the numbers of sides and corners. You can also talk about straight and curved parts of shapes.

★ You can use straight and turning movements.

★ You know that 'angle' is the measure of the size of a turn.

★ When you turn shapes or even turn yourself, you know which turns are right angles.

90°

★ You can measure using non-standard measures (like your hand length or cubes) and using standard measures like these:

centimetre (cm) millilitre (ml) metre (m) litre (l) gram (g) kilogram (kg)	days of the week $\frac{1}{2}$ hours months of the year $\frac{1}{4}$ hours hours minutes seconds

★ You can use a ruler to draw and measure lines to the nearest centimetre.

Data handling

These are the main things you should be able to do if you have achieved Level 2 in data handling.

Level 2

⭐ When you are given a set of objects, you can sort them in different ways and explain how you made your sets.

⭐ You can sort objects using more than one criterion. This means you could find objects that are small **AND** green, or that are square **AND NOT** thin.

⭐ You can gather information by asking people around you and by looking at sets and objects.

⭐ When you record your findings, you can use simple lists, tables and block graphs. Here are some examples:

Chart to show the number of pets we have

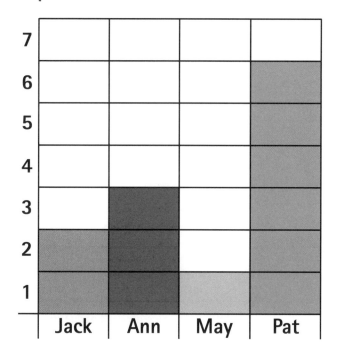

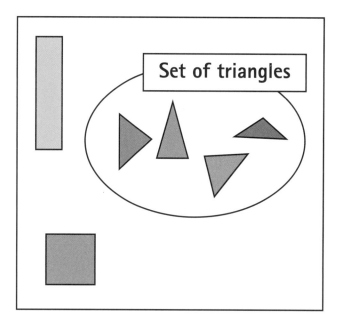

Even numbers	16	24	8	32	
Odd numbers	7	11	25	53	49

Explaining general statements

To achieve Level 3, you need to know how to investigate
statements to find out if they are true or not.

Let's practise!

Question: Wednesday is the favourite day for most
children in Buxworth School. Is this true?
Explain your answer.

1 Read the question, then read it again.
What are you being asked to do?

Find out if most children prefer
Wednesdays.

2 How can you show if this is true?

Collect the information you need –
ask the children at Buxworth
School which day they prefer.

3 What should you do with the
information you collect?

Present it clearly. For data, a bar
chart is a good idea.

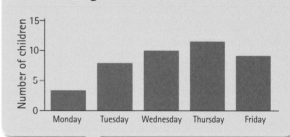

4 Now use the information to
say whether the statement is
true or not.

More children liked Thursday,
so the statement is not true.
Wednesday is not the favourite
day for most children.

5 Check your answer.

Read the statement again.
Make sure your answer refers to
the information you collected
and says whether the statement
is true or not.

TIPS If a statement is not true, you only need to write one
example that shows it isn't true. Make sure your answer
explains why the statement is true or not.

Practice questions

1   Peter thinks your friends prefer to wear black clothes. Is he correct?
    Explain your answer.

2   Is it true that numbers that can be divided by five (without having a remainder)
    always end with a five or a zero? Give a reason for your answer.

3   Do you think Ann is right? Explain your answer.

Adding an odd number to another odd
number gives an odd number.

4   John says he knows that quadrilaterals always have at least one right-angled
    corner. Explain why John is not correct.

5   Liz thinks that multiples of four are always even numbers. Is she correct?
    Explain your answer.

Sequences

Lots of mathematics uses sequences (patterns). At Level 3, you need to be able to find and explain patterns.

Let's practise!

Question: Explain this sequence.
1, 4, 7, 10, 13 ...

(1) Read the question, then read it again. What are you being asked to do?

Find and explain the pattern.

(2) Examine the numbers – are they part of a pattern you know? If yes, go to step 4.

No, they are not all odd or even numbers and they are not all part of a times table I know.

(3) Look at the differences between the numbers.

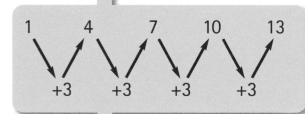

1   4   7   10   13

+3   +3   +3   +3

(4) Explain the pattern.

In this pattern, you keep adding three to the number.

TIP 1 Always check your times tables and any patterns you know first. If it is a pattern you already know, you can save yourself a lot of work!

TIP 2 To check your answer, start with the first number in the sequence and use your 'rule'. If you are right, you will make the same pattern.

Practice questions

1   Write these patterns.

a) Start at six and write the next five even numbers.

b) Write the first six numbers in the three-times table.

c) Start at 16 and count backwards in 3s to 1.

2   Explain these sequences.

a) 5, 10, 15, 20, 25...

b) 1, 3, 5, 7, 9...

c) 2, 6, 10, 14, 18...

d) 50, 47, 44, 41, 39...

e) 1, 2, 4, 8, 16, 32...

Place value and approximations

Remember, the position of each digit in a number is very important. It shows how much the digit is worth.

Use the headings **Th H T U** (Thousands, Hundreds, Tens, Units) to help you work out what each digit is worth.

Let's practise!

> Question: What is the biggest number you can make with the digits 3, 5 and 1?

1 Read the question, then read it again. What are you being asked to do?

Make the biggest number you can with 3, 5 and 1.

2 Think about the place value headings.

With three digits, you need the first three headings: **H T U**.

3 Think which digits need to be paired with which heading.

The largest digit is 5, so that needs to be in the hundreds column.

4 Place all the digits carefully.

The next largest digit is 3, so that should go in the tens column, leaving 1 for the units.

5 Double-check and write in your answer.

531 is the biggest number you can make with 3, 5 and 1.

KEY FACTS
★ At Level 3, the headings for place value are thousands, hundreds, tens and units.

★ The headings are Th H T U.

★ Thousands are worth more than hundreds, which are worth more than tens, which are worth more than units.

TIPS You mostly deal with three-digit numbers at Level 3, so concentrate on understanding H T U.

Practice questions

Achieved?

1   Write the biggest and smallest numbers you can make with these digits.

a) 6 2 5

biggest =   smallest =

b) 1 8 3

biggest =   smallest =

c) 3 0 9

biggest =   smallest =

2   Write these numbers in order of size, the biggest one first.

465   654   645   564

3   Join these numbers to the hundred they round up or down to by drawing a line.

```
                              100
a) 589                        200
                              300
b) 214                        400
                              500
c) 903                        600
                              700
d) 379                        800
                              900
                             1000
```

4   These children count how many steps they walked to school. Then, they each walk ten more steps. How many steps has each child walked in total?

a) Sam, 742   **b)** Andy, 667

c) Lucy, 802   **d)** Laurie, 538

e) Irma, 593

Decimal numbers

Numbers after a decimal point show smaller measures,
e.g. 3.25 m means 3 m and 25 cm, and £4.63 means £4 and 63p.

Let's practise!

Question: Write 5 m and 3 cm as decimal numbers.

(1) Read the question, then read it again.

We need to use a decimal point so that we don't need the smaller measure.

(2) Which measure do we need to use?

The larger measures are metres, so that is what we need to use.

(3) Write the number of the larger measure and put a decimal point.

Write 5.

(4) Work out the tens and units of the smaller measure.

3 cm is 0 tens and 3 units.

(5) Write the tens and units after the decimal point.

Write 5.03.

(6) Remember the units you need for your answer.

The larger measures are metres, so write 5.03 m.

(7) If your answer looks sensible, write it in.

If your answer doesn't look sensible, go back to step 1 and try again.

KEY FACTS Numbers before the decimal point are larger measures (or numbers).

Numbers after the decimal point are smaller measures (or numbers).

TIPS ★ The digits in the answer should be in the same order as the digits in the question, e.g. 5 m and 24 cm = 5.24 m.

★ You will need a zero after the decimal point if there is only one digit for the smaller unit, e.g. £7 and 4p = £7.04.

Practice questions

1 Write these lengths using decimal numbers:

a) 5 m and 24 cm

b) 7 m and 50 m

c) 15 m and 36 cm

d) 9 m and 5 cm

2 Write these amounts of money as decimal numbers.

a) £6 and 52p

b) £8 and 25p

c) £4 and 50p

d) £4 and 5p

3 Write these totals.

a) £3.21 and 30p

b) £5.50 and 6p

c) £6.10 and 73p

4 Circle the correct answer.

a) Josh jumped four times. He measured each jump.
   Which was his longest jump?

   4.52 m   4.25 m   4.05 m   4.50 m

b) These are the price tags on four books.
   Which was the most expensive?

   £2.53   £5.32   £3.52   £5.23

c) John bought four computer games.
   Which was the cheapest?

   £6.69   £9.69   £6.99   £9.96

Negative numbers

When you start from zero and count up as far as you can, do you realise that you can start at zero and count down as well? Numbers less than zero are called negative numbers.

Let's practise!

Question: The thermometer shows that the temperature is −5°C in New York. It is 6°C warmer in London. What is the temperature in London?

1. Read the question, then read it again.

You need to find the temperature 6°C warmer than −5°C.

2. Work out if you need to count up or down from the given number.

If it is warmer, you will need to count up.

3. Draw a thermometer or number staircase.

Draw a number staircase. The starting number of −5°C is at the bottom because you need to count up.

3
2
1
0
−1
−2
−3
−4
−5

4. From the starting number, count up or down the number of steps you need.

It is 6°C warmer, so you need to count up six steps from −5°C. You land on 1°C.

5. Check your answer. If it is correct, write it in the answer box.

Work from step 1 again to check. The answer 1°C is correct, so write it down.

KEY FACTS Negative numbers are worth less than zero. They always have a minus sign (−) in front of them, e.g. −6, −32.

TIPS It is easier to move up and down a number staircase than a thermometer – you are less likely to skip numbers by accident!

Practice questions

1 In the morning, the temperature is –2°C.
It increases 4°C by noon.
What is the temperature at noon?

2 The temperature inside is 8°C. It is 10°C colder outside.
What is the temperature outside?

3 It is 6°C in Paris and –3°C in Moscow. What is the difference in temperature?

4 Complete the number line.

5 The temperature in the freezer is –6°C. Tom changes the setting, so the temperature changes to –2°C.

   a) Is the freezer warmer or colder?

   b) By how much?

Adding three-digit numbers

When you add numbers, it is best to add the units first, then work across to the tens and the hundreds.

Let's practise!

Question: 523 + 295 =

1 Read the question, then read it again.

523 + 295

2 Think about how to set out the calculation.

Using HTU columns is a good way to do this type of sum.

```
H T U
  5 2 3
+ 2 9 5
-------
```

3 Add the units first.

The units are 3 and 5.
3 + 5 = 8

```
H T U
  5 2 3
+ 2 9 5
-------
      8
```

4 Next, add the tens.

The tens are 20 + 90 = 110, so add 100 to the hundreds column. Write it underneath the answer line. Leave the ten in the tens column.

```
H T U
  5 2 3
+ 2 9 5
-------
    1 8
  1
```

5 Finally, add the hundreds.

The hundreds are 5, 2 and 1.
5 + 2 + 1 = 8.

```
H T U
  5 2 3
+ 2 9 5
-------
  8 1 8
  1
```

6 Check your answer.

Our answer looks correct.

Practice questions

Write an estimated answer, then work out these calculations.

	Estimate	Answer
1 456 + 428 =		
2 752 + 164 =		
3 Add 367 and 219.		
4 834 + 128 =		
5 Find the total of 427 and 492.		
6 Increase 476 by 384.		
7 538 plus 374 is ...		
8 545 + 857 =		
9 What is 649 more than 185?		
10 What is the sum of 395 and 486?		

Subtracting three-digit numbers

For Level 3, you need to be able to subtract three-digit numbers.
When you subtract, you may need to 'exchange' numbers with
the next column. This is an important skill to master.

Let's practise!

Question: 671 – 285 = [ ]

(1) Read the question, then read it again.

671 – 285

(2) Think about how to set out the calculation.

Using HTU columns is a good way to do this type of sum.

```
  H T U
    6 7 1
  - 2 8 5
  _____
```

(3) Subtract the units first.

The units are 1 and 5. You can't do 1 – 5, so you 'exchange' a ten for 10 units.

```
  H T U
  6¹⁶7¹1
  - 2 8 5
  _____
        6
```

(4) Next, subtract the tens.

The tens are 60 and 80. You can't do 60 – 80, so you 'exchange' a hundred for 10 tens.

```
    H T U
  ⁵6¹⁶7¹1
  - 2 8 5
  _____
      8 6
```

(5) Finally, subtract the hundreds.

Finally, subtract the hundreds. The hundreds are 500 and 200, so 500 – 200 = 300.

```
    H T U
  ⁵6¹⁶7¹1
  + 2 8 5
  _____
    3 8 6
```

(6) Check your answer.

Our answer looks correct.

Practice questions

Write an estimated answer, then work out these calculations.

	Estimate	Answer

1   453 – 235 =

2   648 – 473 =

3   578 – 249 =

4   496 subtract 315 is ...

5   450 take away 335 is ...

6   Find the difference between
    580 and 268.

7   How many more is 536 than 388?

8   853 minus 675 is ...

9   Decrease 607 by 466.

10   What is the difference between
     973 and 585?

Division problems with remainders

At Level 3, some division problems will have remainders.
You have to work out if the answer needs to be rounded up or not.

Let's practise!

Question: Kim has 24 stickers. She can fit five stickers on every page in her book. How many pages will she need for her animal stickers?

1 Read the question, then read it again. What are you being asked to do?

Find the number of pages needed for 24 stickers.

2 What type of calculation are you being asked to work out?

$24 \div 5$

3 Picture the numbers.

24 is close to 25.
$25 \div 5 = 5$

4 How many stickers will fit on a page?

You need 5 stickers to fill a page.

5 How many pages can she fill?

She has 24 stickers.
$4 \times 5 = 20$ so she can fill 4 pages and she will have 4 stickers left.

6 What happens to the ones left over? Do we need to round up the answer?

They need to be stuck on a page as well, so she needs one extra page. We round the answer up 1.

7 How many pages does she need altogether?

$4 + 1 = 5$ pages.

8 Check your answer.

From step 3, we can see our answer is correct.

TIPS With division problems, always check whether the answer needs to round up one when there are things left over. If five people can travel in a car, you need three cars for twelve people – or some people will be left behind! It can help to draw the problem.

Practice questions

1 Six eggs fit into an egg box. How many boxes will you need for 26 eggs?

  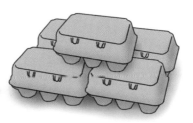

2 Ten crayons fill a pack. How many packs can you fill with 45 crayons?

3 Every box of crayons holds five packs. How many boxes are needed for 52 packs?

4 A coach can carry 50 passengers. There are 280 people going on the club outing. How many coaches will the organiser need to book?

5 Chocolate biscuits are sold in packs of eight. There are 35 children in the class. Mrs Bee gives everyone a chocolate biscuit.

a) How many packs did she need to buy?

b) How many biscuits did she have left over?

Fractions

At Level 3, you need to understand simple fractions and recognise fractions that are equivalent – that means the same. Easy!

Let's practise!

Question: Circle the two fractions that are equivalent: $\frac{1}{2}$　$\frac{1}{3}$　$\frac{2}{5}$　$\frac{2}{4}$　$\frac{1}{4}$

1 Read the question, then read it again.

Find two fractions that are the same.

2 Find a way to look at the fractions.

Draw a square for each fraction. Make your squares the same size.

$\frac{1}{2}$　$\frac{1}{3}$　$\frac{2}{5}$　$\frac{2}{4}$　$\frac{1}{4}$

3 Picture the fractions.

Split each square into the correct number of pieces and shade the fraction. The first one is done.

$\frac{1}{2}$　$\frac{1}{3}$　$\frac{2}{5}$　$\frac{2}{4}$　$\frac{1}{4}$

4 Find the fractions that are the same.

$\frac{1}{2}$ and $\frac{2}{4}$ have the same amount of square coloured, so they must be equivalent.

KEY FACTS
- ★ A fraction is part of a whole. It has two parts. The NUMERATOR tells you how many pieces or groups to use.
- ★ The DENOMINATOR tells you how many equal pieces or groups you need to make, so $\frac{2}{3}$ tells you to make three equal pieces and use two of them.

Practice questions

1   Draw squares in the answer boxes and colour these fractions:

a) $\frac{1}{2}$

b) $\frac{1}{8}$

c) $\frac{2}{6}$

d) $\frac{3}{5}$

2   Circle the biggest fraction.

$\frac{3}{8}$ $\frac{2}{3}$ $\frac{5}{6}$ $\frac{1}{2}$

3   Join the two pairs of equivalent fractions with a line.

$\frac{3}{6}$ $\frac{1}{4}$

$\frac{4}{5}$ $\frac{1}{3}$

$\frac{2}{6}$ $\frac{1}{2}$

4   Fill in the missing numbers to make these fractions equivalent.

a) $\frac{1}{2} = \frac{\boxed{}}{8}$ b) $\frac{\boxed{}}{8} = \frac{1}{4}$ c) $\frac{6}{8} = \frac{\boxed{}}{4}$

5   Put these fractions in order of size, starting with the smallest.

$\frac{1}{3}$ $\frac{1}{5}$ $\frac{1}{2}$ $\frac{1}{4}$ $\frac{1}{10}$

Reflective symmetry and 2-D shape

To achieve Level 3, you need to be able to recognise reflective symmetry. A shape has reflective symmetry if a mirror through the centre of the shape shows the whole shape. You also need to be able to reflect simple shapes in a mirror line.

Let's practise!

Question: Draw the lines of reflective symmetry on this rectangle.

1 Read the question, then read it again. What are you being asked to do?

Find the lines of reflective symmetry.

2 Look for lines of symmetry.

A line of symmetry cuts a shape in half, but be careful – not all halves are lines of symmetry!

3 Use a mirror to test lines of symmetry.

If you put a mirror on a line of symmetry, you will see the shape with the mirror as you do without it. Test these possible lines of symmetry with a mirror.

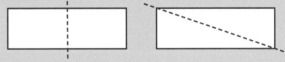

4 Mark any lines of symmetry you find.

The lines of symmetry are:

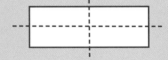

5 Check your answer.

Use your mirror to check the lines you have drawn are lines of symmetry.

TIPS It is important to be accurate. Make sure you check your lines of symmetry AFTER you have drawn them.

Practice questions

1   Draw all the lines of symmetry of these shapes.

a)

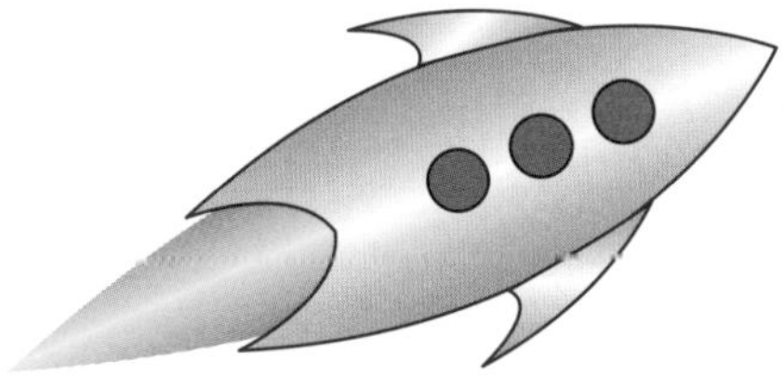

b)

A square always has [ ] lines of symmetry.

c)

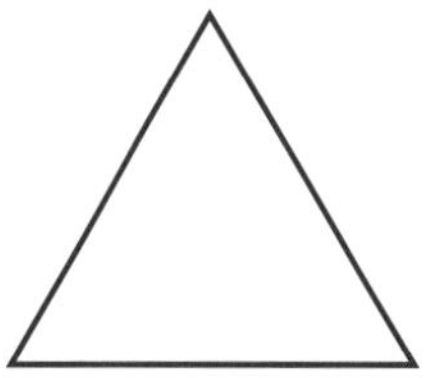

d)

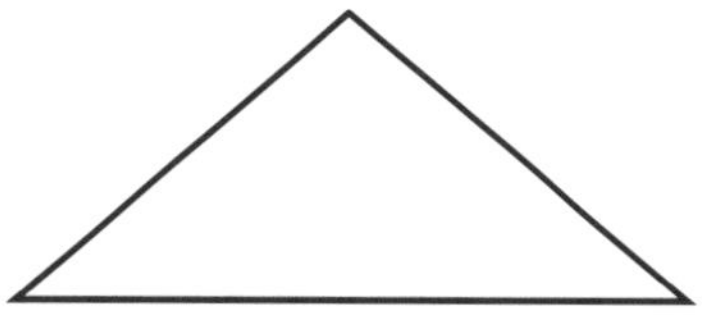

Shape c) is an [   ] triangle because it has [ ] lines of symmetry.

Shape d) is an [   ] triangle because it has [ ] line of symmetry.

e)

f)

This shape is called a [   ] .

g)

2   Complete these pictures so that the dotted line is a line of symmetry.

a)

b)

c)

Name the shape you have made for question c). [   ]

3-D shapes

For Level 3, you need to recognise prisms and pyramids. You also need to describe the faces, edges and vertices on solid shapes.

Let's practise!

Question: Circle the prism and fill in the boxes for the number of faces, edges and vertices it has.

a)   b)   c)   d)

Number of faces   Number of edges   Number of vertices

1   Read the question, then read it again.

Find and describe the prism.

2   What information do you need?

You need to know a prism has the same shape at each end and that they are joined by rectangles.

3   Which shape do you need?

Shape d) has a square at each end joined by rectangles.

4   Have you finished the question?

No, I need to count the number of faces, edges and vertices.

5   Count the faces and the edges.

There are six flat surfaces, so there are six faces. There are 12 edges.

6   Count the vertices.

There are eight corners, so that's eight vertices.

7   Check your answer.

Work through the question again.

KEY FACTS   ★ A vertex is a corner on a 3-D shape or a point. The plural of vertex is vertices.

Practice questions

1   Colour the pyramids red and the prisms blue. Colour all the other shapes yellow.

a)

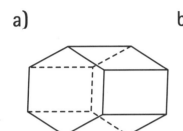

b)

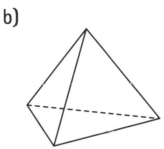

c)

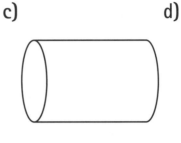

d)

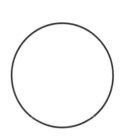

e)

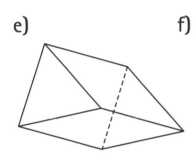

f)

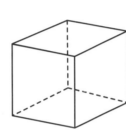

g)

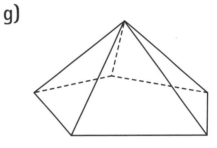

2   A cube has ☐ faces, ☐ edges and ☐ vertices.

3   A square-based pyramid has ☐ faces, ☐ edges and ☐ vertices.

4   A pentagonal prism has ☐ faces, ☐ edges and ☐ vertices.

5   The shape with no vertices, one face and no edges is a ☐ .

6   The shape with one vertex, one edge and two faces is a ☐ .

Length, capacity and mass

To achieve Level 3, you need to know the following things about measures:
a) Which units of measure to use when measuring length, mass and capacity.
b) How to read instruments of measurement, including scales.

Let's practise!

Question: What measurement is shown on the scales?

1 Read the question, then read it again.

Work out the measurement.

2 What information do you need?

You need to know the value of the unlabelled marks on the scale.

3 What value do the numbers represent and where is the pointer pointing?

The units on the scale are in kilograms. The pointer is between 3 and 4 kg.

4 What is the value of the unlabelled marks?

There are four sections between the kilograms, so each section is worth one quarter of a kilogram.

$1\,kg = 1000\,g$, so $\frac{1}{4}\,kg = 250\,g$.

5 What measurement is shown?

The third mark between 3 kg and 4 kg is 3 and $\frac{3}{4}$ kg or 3 kg and 750 g.

6 Check your answer.

Read the question and look at the scale again to check.

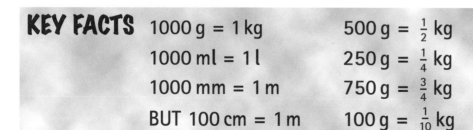

KEY FACTS

1000 g = 1 kg	500 g = $\frac{1}{2}$ kg
1000 ml = 1 l	250 g = $\frac{1}{4}$ kg
1000 mm = 1 m	750 g = $\frac{3}{4}$ kg
BUT 100 cm = 1 m	100 g = $\frac{1}{10}$ kg

Practice questions

Write the measurements shown on these scales.

1

2

3

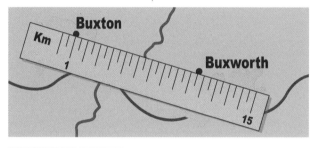

4

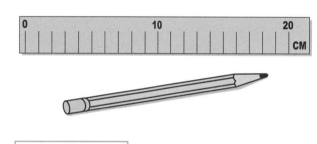

5

6

7

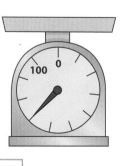

8

Measurement problems

Some of the problems you are given at Level 3
involve using measurement.

Let's practise!

Question: A rope is 36 m long. Andrew wants to
cut 5 m lengths. How many
5 m lengths can he cut
from the 36 m rope?

1 Read the question, then read it again. What are you being asked to do?

Find out how many 5 m lengths can be cut from a 36 m length of rope.

2 What calculation do you need to do?

You need to share 36 by 5, so 36 ÷ 5.

3 Study the numbers again and think about the answer you would expect.

You know the answer should be about 35 ÷ 5 = 7.

4 Work out the calculation you need to do. What answer do you get?

36 ÷ 5 = 7 r1

5 What does the answer tell you?

Andrew can cut seven lengths and there will be 1 m of rope left.

6 What is the answer to the question?

Andrew can cut seven lengths.

7 Check your answer.

From step 3, we know our answer should be about seven. Our answer looks correct.

KEY FACTS Problems are solved by adding, subtracting, multiplying or dividing the numbers. You can use any method you like to calculate your answer.

TIPS ★ Act like a detective to find the calculation in disguise.
★ Always think about the answer you would expect. Use this to help work out whether you need to +, −, x or ÷.
★ Remember to check that the units are on your answer.

Practice questions

1   Mary has a bucket that holds 3l of water.
    Her sister's paddling pool holds 35 l of water.
    How many buckets of water will Mary need to
    fill the paddling pool?

2   Tim packs raisins into $\frac{1}{2}$ kg packs. He puts 15 packs into a box.

    a) What will the total weight of the raisins be?

    b) If the box weighs $\frac{1}{4}$ kg, what will be the
       total weight of the box and the raisins?

3   Alex has six ribbons that are each 50 cm long.
    What is the total length of the ribbons?

4   Helen throws a ball 9 m and Ricky throws a ball 16 m.

    a) What is the total distance the ball is thrown?

    b) What is the difference between the distances?

5   Sam mixes 200 g of flour with 150 g of butter and 50 g of sugar.

    a) What is the total weight of
       Sam's mixture?

    b) How much more flour does
       he use than butter?

    c) If he made three times the amount of mixture,
       how much sugar does he need to use?

6   Mark has to cycle 254 km. He cycles 174 km.
    How much further does he have to go?

Time

For Level 3, you must be able to read analogue and digital time.

Let's practise!

Question: Match the time on each analogue clock to the time on each digital clock by drawing a line.

a)

b)

c)

1   `2:40`

2   `2:20`

3   `3:20`

---

1   Read the question, then read it again.

Match the times.

2   What information do you need?

You need to know how to read analogue and digital clock times.

3   Look at the analogue clocks and work out which hour they last went PAST.

- Clock a) is past three and clock 3) is the only digital clock showing three hours.
- Clocks b) and c) both went past two and both clocks 1) and 2) show two hours.

4   For questions with two possible answers, check the minutes from 12.

Clock b) is 40 minutes past and clock c) is 20 minutes past.

5   Use the information to find the answer.

Clock a) shows the same time as clock 3). Clock b) is 40 minutes past, so that must be clock 1). That means clock c) must be clock 2).

6   Check your answer.

Work out the time on each clock to check your answer.

Practice questions

1 Write these analogue times in two different ways. The first one is done for you.

a)

quarter to 11
10:45

b)

c)

d)

e)

f)

2 Match the times that are the same by drawing a line.

4:10 a.m.   20 past 10

5:45 p.m.   10 to 4

10:20 a.m.   10 past 4

3:50 p.m.   quarter to 6

3 Circle the time above you are mostly likely to be asleep.

Tables and lists

Data is put into tables and lists to make it easy to read.

Let's practise!

Question:
Ben sorted his film character cards.

Film	Number of cards
Harry Potter	7
Ice Age	18
Happy Feet	9
Shrek	14

How many more cards does he have for Shrek than for Harry Potter?

1 Read the question, then read it again. What are you being asked to do?

Find the difference in the number of cards for Shrek and Harry Potter.

2 What information do you need?

There are 14 Shrek cards and 7 Harry Potter cards.

3 What do you need to do?

Decide on the calculation. It's subtraction.

4 Do the calculation.

14 − 7 = 7

5 What is the answer?

He has 7 more Shrek cards than Harry Potter cards.

6 Check your answer by working through the problem again and checking your numbers.

KEY FACTS A tally is a group of five. Four sticks go down and the fifth is drawn across them.

Tallying makes it easy to count data because it is easy to count in fives.

₦₦₦ ₦₦₦ ₦₦₦ ₦₦₦ III

5, 10, 15, 20 and 3 more makes 23.

TIP Look carefully at tables. It is easy to copy the wrong number when you are looking for data. Place a ruler under each line of data to help you read across it.

Practice questions

1   Use this table to answer the questions below.

Team	Supporters
Raiders	17
Strangers	25
Tigers	38
Blurs	14

a) Which is the most popular team?

b) How many supporters are there altogether for Blurs and Strangers?

c) How many more supporters are there for Tigers than Raiders?

d) How many supporters are there altogether?

2   Complete this table and use it to answer the questions below.

Favourite game	Tally of votes	Total
Darts	ЖЖ lll	
Football		18
Snooker	ЖЖ ЖЖ ЖЖ ЖЖ l	
Rounders		24
Cricket	ЖЖ ЖЖ ЖЖ	

a) What is the least popular game?

b) Which games have more than 20 votes?

c) How many people prefer indoor games?

d) How many more people prefer football to cricket?

e) How many people prefer snooker or rounders?

Pictograms

At Level 3, each symbol on a pictogram can represent several units.

Let's practise!

Question: How many oak and horse chestnut trees were seen altogether? Look at the pictograms in the table to work out the answer.

Key

| = 4 trees | | = 2 trees |
| = 3 trees | | = 1 tree |

Type of tree	Number seen
oak	
horse chesnut	
ash	
sycamore	

1 Read the question, then read it again. What are you being asked to do?

Find the total number of oak and horse chestnut trees.

2 What information do you need for this?

You need to know how many oak trees and how many horse chestnut trees were seen.

3 Work out the numbers you need.

The key says each square is worth four. The oak has six full squares: 6 x 4 = 24. It has half a square as well: half of 4 = 2. So the total number of oak trees is 26. The total number of horse chestnut trees is 7.

4 What calculation do you need to do?

An addition. 26 + 7 = 33

5 What is the answer?

In total, 33 oak and horse chestnut trees were seen.

6 Check your answer by working through the problem again.

TIPS Jot down the numbers as you work them out – it makes it easier and quicker to check your answer.

Practice questions

1   Use this table to answer
    the questions below.

Key

◯ = 6 goals

Day	Number of goals scored
Monday	⚽ ⚽
Tuesday	⚽ ⚽ ⚽ ◖
Wednesday	⚽ ⚽ ⚽ ⚽ ⚽
Thursday	
Friday	⚽ ⚽ ⚽ ⚽ ◖

a) How many goals were scored on Tuesday?

b) On which day were 12 goals scored?

c) On Thursday, 15 goals were scored. Fill in the pictogram for Thursday.

d) How many more goals were scored on Wednesday than Monday?

e) On which day(s) were fewer than ten goals scored?

f) Which two days have the highest number of goals?

g) How many goals do these two days have altogether?

2   Emma is drawing a pictogram of the number of questions each person gets
    wrong in the school quiz. She uses a ✗ for her symbol.

    Anne gets 10 questions wrong. How would Emma show this if:

    a) ✗ = 2 questions?

    b) ✗ = 4 questions?

    c) ✗ = 5 questions?

Bar charts

Drawing and interpreting bar charts is a Level 3 skill.

Let's practise!

Question:
This bar chart is not drawn correctly.
Circle the errors.

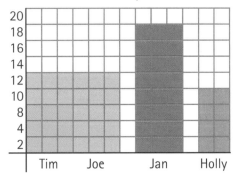

A bar chart to show the amount of money each child raised on a sponsored walk

| | Tim | Joe | Jan | Holly |

---

(1) Read the question, then read it again.

Find the errors in the bar chart.

(2) What information do you need?

You need to know how to draw a bar chart.

(3) Are the title and the axes labelled correctly?

The title is correct but the axes labels are missing. On the vertical axis, the numbers go up in twos but the number six is missing.

(4) Are the bars correct?

- The first and third bars are correct.
- The second bar should be a rectangle above the name.
- The fourth bar is a different width to the other bars.

(5) Any other mistakes?

Yes – there should be a gap of one square between the first and second bars.

(6) Circle all the errors you found.

Make sure you don't forget anything. Work through your list!

Practice questions

1 a) Use the information below and a piece of squared paper to draw your own bar chart.

Our favourite birthday treats	
Ten-pin bowling	14
Swimming	10
Cinema	23
Adventure playground	15

   b) Explain how you decided on the scale for the vertical axis.

   c) Explain how you decided on the width for each bar.

   d) Use this checklist to mark your bar chart. Give yourself a score:
      ➤ if you gave it a title including the words 'favourite birthday treats' **(1 mark)**
      ➤ if you labelled the vertical axis, e.g. 'number of people/children' **(1 mark)**
      ➤ if you labelled the horizontal axis, e.g. 'treat/type of treat' **(1 mark)**
      ➤ if you used a regular scale on your vertical axis **(1 mark)**
      ➤ if your scale makes it easy to read the bar heights **(1 mark)**
      ➤ for each bar that is the same width **(4 marks maximum)**
      ➤ for each bar with the correct treat written underneath **(4 marks maximum)**
      ➤ for each bar that is rectangular **(4 marks maximum)**
      ➤ if your graph fills your paper well **(1 mark)**.

My total score is [   ] out of 18.

Multiplication facts to 10 X 10

Achieved?

For Level 4, you need to know your table facts well.

Let's practise!

Question: Answer these as quickly as you can.

a) 3 X 9 =

b) 7 X 6 =

1 Read the question, then read it again. What are you being asked to do?

Write the answers for the multiplications.

2 Look at the first sum. Do you KNOW the answer?

If you don't know the answer, think of a way to work it out.

3 How could you work out the answer?

You could count up through the table. Use a table fact you know to help you work it out, e.g. 3 X 10 = 30, so 3 X 9 is one '3' less than 30. 3 X 9 = 27.

4 Look at the second sum. Do you KNOW the answer?

If you know the answer, write it down. If not, think of a way to work out the answer.

5 How could you work out the answer?

You could count up through the table. You could use a table fact you know to help you work out the answer. 7 X 5 = 35, so 7 X 6 is a 7 more than 35. And 7 X 6 = 42.

6 Check your answers.

TIPS Learn your multiplication facts in as many ways as you can. Rapping them to music is a good idea!

Finding area and perimeter

For Level 4, you have to find areas and perimeters of shapes drawn on cm-squared paper.

Let's practise!

Question: Find the area and perimeter of this shape.

1 Read the question, then read it again.

Find the area and perimeter.

2 How do you work out the area?

Count the number of squares inside the shape.

3 What is the area?

There are 8 squares inside the shape, so the area is 8 cm².

4 How do you work out the perimeter?

Count the number of square sides on the outside of the shape.

5 What is the perimeter?

There are 12 square sides round the outside, so the perimeter is 12 cm.

6 Check your answer.

Practice question

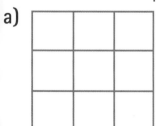

Find the area and perimeter of:

a)

b)

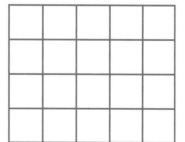

area: perimeter: area: perimeter:

Short division

Short division is a good way to work out division sums.

Let's practise!

Question: 72 ÷ 3 = [   ]

1 Read the question, then read it again.

72 ÷ 3

2 Think about how to set out the calculation.

Draw a 'division' shelter. The first number goes inside the shelter. The second goes in front.

3) 7 2

3 How do you start working through the division?

Work out how many threes there are in the first digit inside the shelter. There are 2 threes and 1 left over. Write 2 on the answer line and put 1 in front of the next digit.

$$\frac{2}{3) 7^{1}2}$$

4 What is the next step?

Work out how many threes there are in the next digit. There are 4 threes, so write the answer.

$$\frac{2\ 4}{3) 7^{1}2}$$

5 What is the answer?

24

6 Check your answer.

Check your answer by multiplying 3 and 24. 3 X 24 = 72

Calculators

Achieved?

Use a calculator to carry out one-step and two-step calculations involving all four operations, recognise negative numbers in the display, correct mistaken entries and interpret the display correctly in the context of money.

Let's practise!

Question: There are 26 children in Year 6. Mrs Hartley buys everyone in Year 6 a book. The books cost £2.65 each. What is the total cost?

1 Read the question, then read it again.

Find the total cost of the books.

2 Think about which calculation you need to do.

There are 26 books and they each cost £2.65. That is 26 lots of £2.65 so you have to multiply.

3 Write down the calculation.

Write 26 X £2.65

4 What is the next step?

Press the keys in the correct order.

2 6 X 2 · 6 5 =

5 What answer is shown?

The calculator screen shows: 68.9

6 How will you write the answer?

It was 26 lots of £2.65 so the answer is in money – £68.90. We add the zero in the pennies column because the answer was £68 and 9 ten-pence coins.

7 Check your answer.

Do the sum again on the calculator.

Test A (non-calculator paper)

1) Write the number that has six units, four tens and three hundreds.

1 mark

2) Join the numbers to the nearest 100 with a line.

475

584

430

552

600

500

400

3 marks

3) Look at this shape.

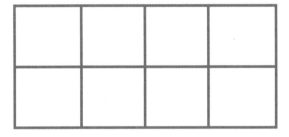

a) Colour $\frac{3}{4}$ of the shape.

1 mark

b) Write a fraction that is equivalent to $\frac{3}{4}$.

1 mark

4) 235 + 147 =

2 marks

5) Double these numbers.

a) 8

b) 31

c) 44

d) 27

4 marks

6 On his birthday, Jim got 14 cards at home. Another three came in the post and he was given five more at school. How many cards did he have altogether?

2 marks

7 Complete these calculations.

a) 6 x 60 =

b) 80 x 3 =

b) 20 ÷ 4 =

d) 190 ÷ 2 =

4 marks

8 Mike reads four pages of a book every day. If there are 32 pages in the book, how many days will it take him to read all the book?

2 marks

9 Draw a quadrilateral, which has exactly two right angles.

2 marks

10   628 – 257 = [   ]

2 marks

11   Bouncy balls cost 40p each. Jack buys 6 bouncy balls. How much does he have to pay?

[   ]

2 marks

12

a) Name this shape.   [   ]

1 mark

b) The shape has [   ] vertices.

1 mark

c) Tick all the faces that are needed to make this shape.

2 marks

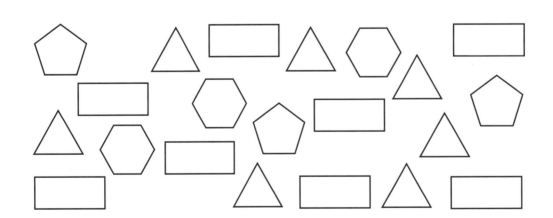

13 It is −4°C outside.
It is 5°C warmer inside.
What is the temperature inside?

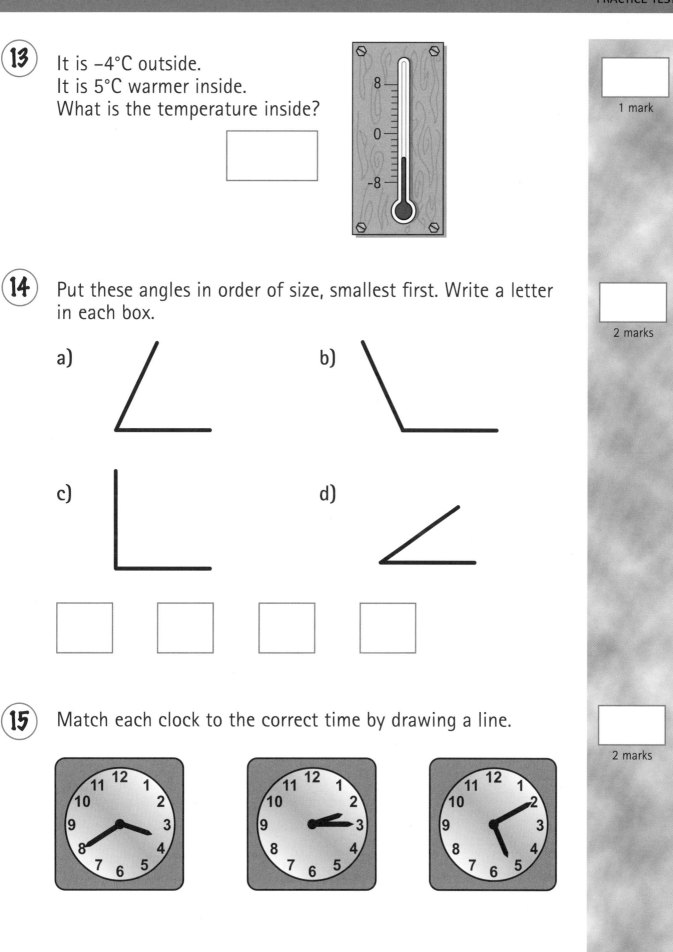

1 mark

14 Put these angles in order of size, smallest first. Write a letter in each box.

a)

b)

c)

d)

2 marks

15 Match each clock to the correct time by drawing a line.

2:15   5:10   3:40

2 marks

16 James walks 5 km.
How many metres has he walked?

2 marks

17 Write each number in the correct section of the
Venn diagram.

3 marks

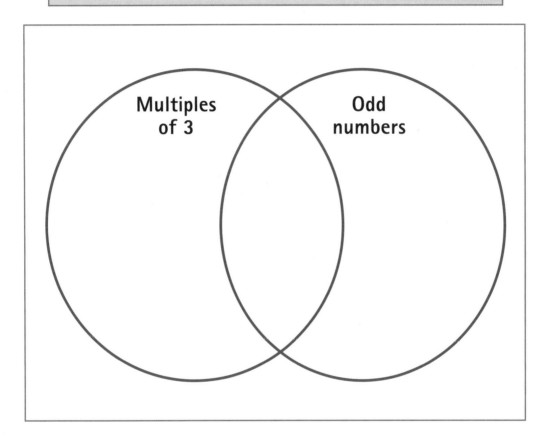

| 6 | 7 | 30 | 21 | 9 | 23 | 14 |

Multiples of 3

Odd numbers

18 Jo saves £2 a week to buy an MP3 player. If the MP3 player
she wants costs £25, how many weeks will it be before she
can buy it?

1 mark

19 Sally is 123 cm tall. Jack is 38 cm taller. How tall is Jack?

1 mark

20 It takes 40 minutes to bake a cake. Sam's cake finishes cooking at half past three.

a) What time did he put it in the oven?

1 mark

b) If it took him 40 minutes to make the cake mixture, how many hours and minutes did it take altogether to make and bake the cake?

1 mark

c) Mary's cake has to be ready at 11 o'clock. If she takes as long as Sam to make and bake it, at what time does she need to start?

1 mark

Test B (calculator paper)

1 Use these digit cards to answer the questions.

2 **7** **5**

a) What is the largest number you can make using all these digit cards?

1 mark

b) What is the smallest number you can make using all these digit cards?

1 mark

2 Ann spent 70p at the shop. Emma spent 37p.

a) How much more did Ann spend than Emma?

1 mark

b) How much change did Ann get from £5?

2 marks

3 Write three addition sums which have an answer of 15.

2 marks

4 There are 30 children in a class. How many groups can they make if there are:

a) five children in a group?

1 mark

b) three children in group?

1 mark

c) four children in a group?

1 mark

5 Complete the calculations.

a) 72 − ☐ = 45

1 mark

b) ☐ + 58 = 85

1 mark

6 School sells CDs for £3 each. How many do they need to sell to raise £87?

2 marks

7 Sally thinks of a number. She multiplies it by 2 and adds 4. The answer is 10. What was the number?

2 marks

8 Look at Shape A.

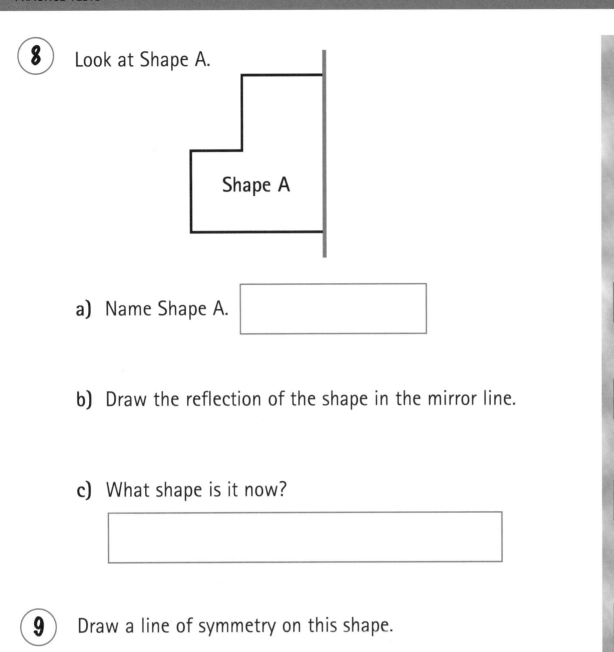

Shape A

a) Name Shape A. [   ]

1 mark

b) Draw the reflection of the shape in the mirror line.

2 marks

c) What shape is it now?

[   ]

1 mark

9 Draw a line of symmetry on this shape.

1 mark

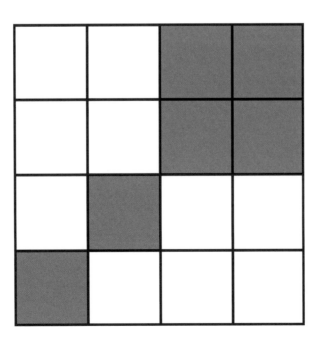

10 Circle the prisms.

a)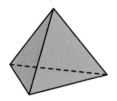

b)

c)

d)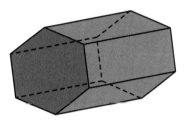

1 mark

11 Circle the largest amount of money.

£4.86   £4.79   £4.96   £4.77

1 mark

12 Look at the co-ordinates.

a) Name the red square.

b) Give the compass direction of the stripy square from the red square.

1 mark

1 mark

1 mark

c) From the red square move 2 east, 3 north, 1 west and 2 south. In which square do you finish?

2 marks

13 Write these measurements as decimals.

a) 5 m 34 cm =

b) 2 m 40 cm =

1 mark

1 mark

14 Answer the questions using the scales.

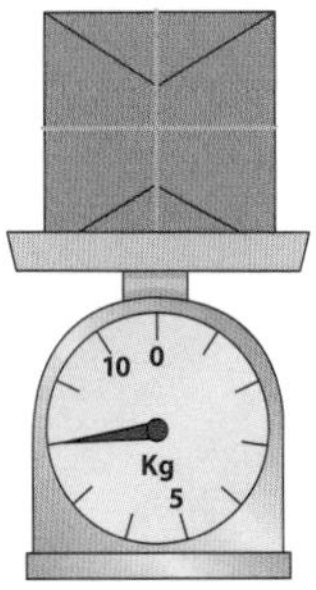

a) How many kg does the box weigh?

1 mark

b) How many grams does the box weigh?

1 mark

15 Four boxes are delivered to Buxworth School.
They weigh 19 kg, 36 kg, 47 kg and 21 kg.

a) What is the total weight of the boxes?

2 marks

b) What is the difference between the heaviest and lightest boxes?

2 marks

c) Which two boxes have a total weight of 66 kg?

2 marks

16 Use the Carroll diagram to answer the questions.

	Plays chess	Does not play chess
Goes swimming	Fran Billy	Katy
Does not go swimming	Haziz	John Jaqua

a) Which children like to swim?

1 mark

b) Which children do not play chess or go swimming?

1 mark

c) Irma likes chess but doesn't go swimming. Write her name in the correct part of the Carroll diagram.

1 mark

17 John bought four CDs. They cost £4.99 each. How much did he spend altogether?

1 mark

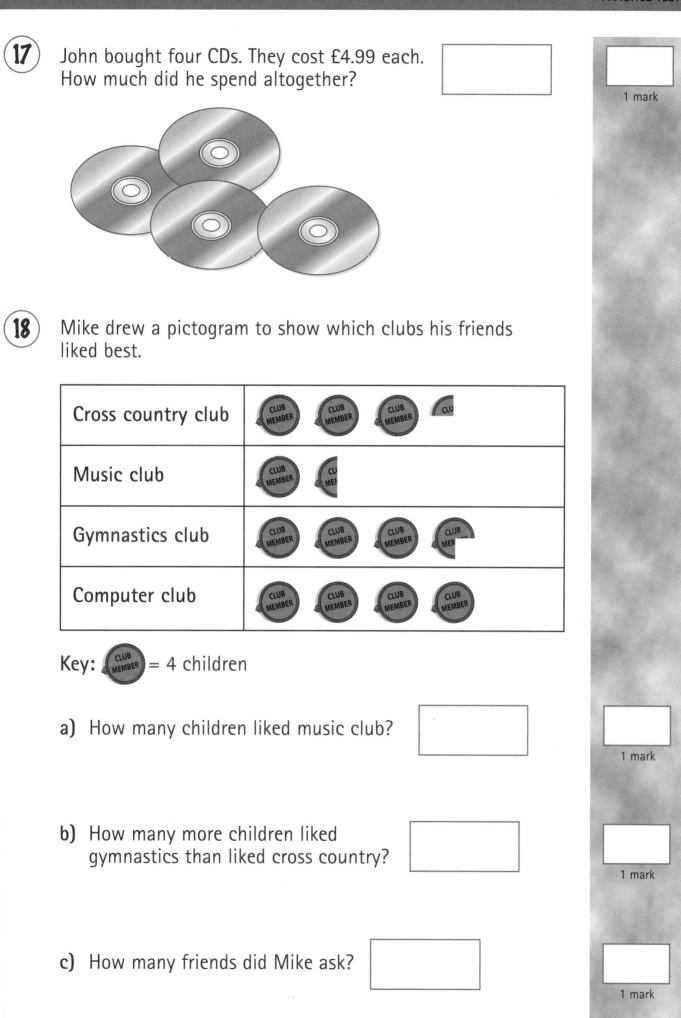

18 Mike drew a pictogram to show which clubs his friends liked best.

Cross country club	CLUB MEMBER CLUB MEMBER CLUB MEMBER CLU
Music club	CLUB MEMBER CLU MEM
Gymnastics club	CLUB MEMBER CLUB MEMBER CLUB MEMBER CLUB MEM
Computer club	CLUB MEMBER CLUB MEMBER CLUB MEMBER CLUB MEMBER

Key: CLUB MEMBER = 4 children

a) How many children liked music club?

1 mark

b) How many more children liked gymnastics than liked cross country?

1 mark

c) How many friends did Mike ask?

1 mark

Answers

Page 11

1 Answers will vary, e.g. true, because when my friends can choose what they wear they usually wear black **or** false, my friends hardly ever wear black.

2 True, e.g. if you count up in fives the numbers always end with a 5 or 0.

3 No, e.g. 1 and 3 are both odd numbers but 1 + 3 = 4, which is even.

4 Pupils should show a drawing of a quadrilateral without a right angle or explain that a quadrilateral doesn't always have a right angle.

5 Yes, the number 4 is a multiple of 2, so all multiples of 4 will be multiples of 2 and multiples of 2 are always even numbers.

Page 13

1 a) 6, 8, 10, 12, 14, 16
b) (0), 3, 6, 9, 12, 15, (18)
c) 16, 13, 10, 7, 4, 1

2 a) multiples of 5/difference of 5/keep adding 5 starting at 5
b) odd numbers starting from 1
c) start at 2 and keep adding 4
d) start at 50 and keep subtracting/count backwards in 3s
e) start at 1 and keep doubling the last number

Page 15

1 a) biggest = 652; smallest = 256
b) biggest = 831; smallest = 138
c) biggest = 930; smallest = 039

2 654, 645, 564, 465

3 a) 600   b) 200   c) 900   d) 400

4 a) 752   b) 677   c) 812   d) 548   e) 603

Page 17

1 a) 5.24 m   b) 7.5 m (allow 7.50 m)
c) 15.36 m   d) 9.05 m

2 Do not allow if £ and p signs both used.
a) £6.52
b) £8.25
c) £4.50 (do not allow £4.5)
d) £4.05

3 a) £3.51   b) £5.56   c) £6.83

4 a) 4.52m   b) £5.32   c) £6.69

Page 19

1 2°C

2 -2°C

3 9°C

4

```
 -5  -4 -3  -2 -1   0   1   2   3   4   5   6   7
  •   •   •   •   •   •   •   •   •   •   •   •   •
```

5 a) warmer   b) (+) 4°C

Page 21

1 900; 884

2 1000; 916

3 600; 586

4 900; 962

5 900; 919

6 900; 860

7 900; 912

8 1400; 1402

9 800; 834

10 900; 881

Page 23

1 300; 218   **6** 300; 312

2 100; 175   **7** 100; 148

3 400; 329   **8** 200; 178

4 200; 181   **9** 100; 141

5 200; 115   **10** 400; 388

Page 25

1 five boxes (do not allow four boxes)

2 four packs (do not allow five packs)

3 11 packs (do not allow ten packs)

4 six coaches (do not allow five coaches)

5 a) five packs   b) five biscuits

Page 27

1 a)   b)

c)   d)

2 $\frac{5}{6}$

3 $\frac{3}{6}$ and $\frac{1}{2}$; $\frac{2}{6}$ and $\frac{1}{3}$

4 a) 4   b) 2   c) 3

5 $\frac{1}{10}$, $\frac{1}{5}$, $\frac{1}{4}$, $\frac{1}{3}$, $\frac{1}{2}$

Page 29

Page 29

1 a) one line of symmetry

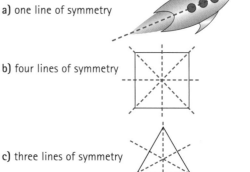

b) four lines of symmetry

c) three lines of symmetry

Shape **c)** is an equilateral triangle because it has 3 lines of symmetry.

d) one line of symmetry

Shape **d)** is an isosceles triangle because it has 1 line of symmetry.

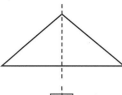

e) four lines of symmetry

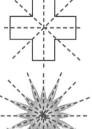

f) eight lines of symmetry

g) No lines of symmetry

This shape is called a quadrilateral (or a parallelogram).

2 a)

b)

c)

The shape you have made for question **c)** is a hexagon.

Page 31

1 a), e), f) blue prisms;
b), g) red pyramids;
c), d) yellow other shapes (cylinder, sphere)

2 A cube has 6 faces, 12 edges and 8 vertices.

3 A square-based pyramid has 5 faces, 8 edges and 5 vertices.

4 A pentagonal prism has 7 faces, 15 edges and 10 vertices.

5 sphere

6 cone

Page 33

1 $8\frac{1}{2}$ litres

2 $1\frac{3}{4}$ kg

3 $9\frac{1}{2}$ km

4 $15\frac{1}{2}$ cm

5 200 g

6 1.4 l or 1 l and 400 ml

7 70 g

8 80 ml

Page 35

1 12 (do not allow 11)

2 a) $7\frac{1}{2}$ kg   **b)** $7\frac{3}{4}$ kg

3 300 cm or 3 m

4 a) 25 m   **b)** 7 m

5 a) 400 g   **b)** 50 g   **c)** 150 g

6 80 km

Page 37

1 a) quarter to 11; 10:45
b) half past 7; 7:30
c) 10 to 5; 4:50
d) 25 to 1; 12:35
e) 20 past 9; 9:20
f) 10 past 10; 10:10

2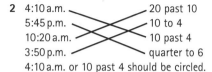

4:10 a.m.   20 past 10
5:45 p.m.   10 to 4
10:20 a.m.   10 past 4
3:50 p.m.   quarter to 6

4:10 a.m. or 10 past 4 should be circled.

Page 39

1 a) Tigers   **b)** 39   **c)** 21   **d)** 94

2

Favourite game	Tally of votes	Total
Darts	ⵌ III	8
Football	ⵌ ⵌ ⵌ III	18
Snooker	ⵌ ⵌ ⵌ ⵌ I	21
Rounders	ⵌ ⵌ ⵌ ⵌ IIII	24
Cricket	ⵌ ⵌ ⵌ	15

a) darts   **b)** snooker and rounders
c) 29   **d)** 3   **e)** 45

Page 41

1 a) 21

b) Monday

c) (footballs)

d) 18

e) None

f) Wednesday and Friday

g) 57

2 a) ✗ ✗ ✗ ✗ ✗   **b)** ✗ ✗ ✗

c) ✗ ✗

Page 43

1 a)

(bar chart: Number of children vs Type of treat)
Ten-pin bowling ≈ 14, Swimming ≈ 10, Cinema ≈ 23, Adventure playground ≈ 15

b) By checking the highest number needed, the other numbers (for factors) and the number of squares available.

c) By checking the number of bars needed and the width of the paper.

d) The maximum score you can achieve is 18 marks.

Page 45

a) area = 9 cm²; perimeter = 12 cm

b) area = 20 cm²; perimeter = 18 cm

Page 48

Test A (non–calculator paper)

1) 346 *(1 mark)*

2)

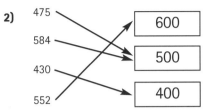

475 → 500
584 → 600
430 → 400
552 → 500

(1 mark for two correct, 2 marks for three correct, 3 marks for all correct)

3) a) any 6 squares coloured *(1 mark)*

b) any fraction that is equivalent to $\frac{3}{4}$, e.g. $\frac{6}{8}$, $\frac{9}{12}$, $\frac{12}{16}$, $\frac{30}{40}$, etc *(1 mark)*

4) 382

(2 marks for correct answer, 1 mark for incorrect answer but evidence of correct working out)

5) a) 16 *(1 mark)*   b) 62 *(1 mark)*
c) 88 *(1 mark)*   d) 54 *(1 mark)*

6) 22

(2 marks for correct answer, 1 mark for incorrect answer but evidence of correct working out)

7) a) 360 *(1 mark)* b) 240 *(1 mark)*
c) 5 *(1 mark)*   d) 95 *(1 mark)*

8) 8 days

(2 marks for correct answer, 1 mark for incorrect answer but evidence of correct working out)

9) This is one example of a quadrilateral with two right angles.

(1 mark for drawing a quadrilateral, 1 mark for drawing a a quadrilateral with two right angles)

10) 371

(2 marks for correct answer, 1 mark for incorrect answer but evidence of correct working out)

11) £2.40 or 240p (not £2.40p)

(2 marks for correct answer, 1 mark for incorrect answer but evidence of correct working out)

12) a) a (pentagonal) prism *(1 mark)*
b) ten vertices *(1 mark)*
c) You need to tick two pentagons and five rectangles.
(2 marks for correct answer, 1 mark if only pentagons and rectangles are ticked but the numbers are incorrect)

13) 1°C *(1 mark)*

14) d), a), c), b)

(2 marks for correct answer, 1 mark for at least two angles correctly ordered)

15)

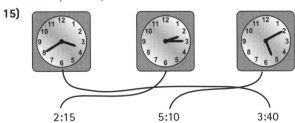

2:15   5:10   3:40

(2 marks for correct answer, 1 mark if answer partially correct)

16) 5000 m

(2 marks for correct answer, 1 mark if units are missed off)

17)

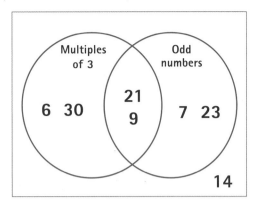

Multiples of 3 — 6 30
21 9
Odd numbers — 7 23
14

(3 marks for all numbers correctly placed, 2 marks for at least five numbers correctly placed, 1 mark for at least three numbers correctly placed)

18) 13 weeks *(1 mark)*

19) 161 cm or 1 m and 61 cm *(1 mark)*

20) a) 2:50 or 10 to 3 *(1 mark)*
b) 1 hour and 20 minutes *(1 mark)*
c) 9:40 or 20 to 10 *(1 mark)*

Page 54

Test B (calculator paper)

1) a) 752 *(1 mark)*   b) 257 *(1 mark)*

2) a) 33p *(1 mark)*

b) £4.30 or 430p

(2 marks for correct answer, 1 mark for incorrect answer but evidence of correct working out)

3) Choose three from 15+0, 14+1, 13+2, 12+3, 11+4, 10+5, 9+6, 8+7, 7+8, 6+9, 5+10, 4+11, 3+12, 2+13, 1+14, 0+15
(1 mark for two sums correct, 2 marks for three sums correct)

4) a) 6 *(1 mark)*   b) 10 *(1 mark)*
c) 7 (with 2 left over) *(1 mark)*

5) a) 27 *(1 mark)*   b) 27 *(1 mark)*

6) 29 CDs
(2 marks for correct answer, 1 mark for incorrect answer but evidence of correct working out)

7) 3
(2 marks for correct answer, 1 mark for incorrect answer but evidence of correct working out)

8) a) (irregular) hexagon *(1 mark)*

b)

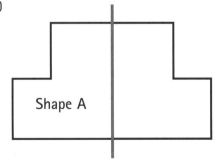

Shape A

(2 marks for completely correct reflection, 1 mark for inaccurate reflection)

c) (irregular) octagon

(1 mark – allow mark if incorrect attempt at reflection but the shape created is correctly named)

9)

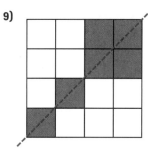

(1 mark)

10)

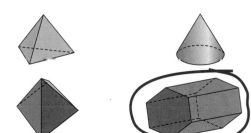

(1 mark)

11) £4.96 *(1 mark)*

12) a) (2, 1) *(1 mark)*

b) north-west *(1 mark)*

c) (3, 2)

(2 marks for correct answer, 1 mark for incorrect answer but evidence of correct working out)

13) a) 5.34 m *(1 mark)*   b) 2.40 m *(1 mark)*

14) a) 8 kg *(1 mark)*

b) 8000 g *(1 mark)*

15) a) 123 kg

(2 marks for correct answer, 1 mark for incorrect answer but evidence of correct working out)

b) 28 kg

(2 marks for correct answer, 1 mark for incorrect answer but evidence of correct working out)

c) 19 kg and 47 kg *(1 mark)*

16) a) Fran, Billy and Katy *(1 mark for all)*

b) John and Jaqua *(1 mark for both)*

c) Irma's name should be written in the same box as Haziz's name. *(1 mark)*

17) £19.96 *(1 mark)*

18) a) 6 *(1 mark)*

b) 2 *(1 mark)*

c) 50 *(1 mark)*